ISBN 1 870870 867

Published in Great Britain by John Brown Publishing Limited
The Boathouse, Crabtree Lane, Fulham, London SW6 8NJ.

Second printing November 1996

Printed and bound in Great Britain.

THE VIZ BOOK OF CRAP JOKES

A COMPILATION OF PISS-POOR QUALITY SECOND HAND, THIRD RATE JOKES FROM THE PAGES OF VIZ MAGAZINE

Cobbled together hurriedly by Chris Donald
Simon Thorp, Graham Dury & Simon Donald

*With special thanks to Roger Radio
Jim Biz, Brent Russell, Tony Harding
and everyone else who contributed to this book*

HOW TO ENJOY YOUR NEW BOOK OF JOKES

Congratulations. You are now the owner of possibly the world's greatest collection of poor qual
jokes. If read correctly this book will probably give you several minutes of pleasure. Here are a f
tips to help you get the most from your book of crap jokes.

1 Make sure you are comfortable, relaxed and in a pleasant frame of mind before attempting
read any jokes. (Perhaps you'd like to make yourself a cup of tea or coffee if you prefer, a
settle back with a biscuit or scone in your favourite armchair). Try to wear loose and comfortab
clothing whenever possible. Take the phone off the hook, and remove the batteries from your do
bell.

2 Pace yourself properly. Don't try to read too many jokes in one go. Read two or three to beg
with, then give yourself a break. Stretch your legs, take the dog for a walk. On your return y
will feel refreshed and ready to continue. Under no circumstances should you attempt to read t
entire book in one session.

3 If you feel that you have not enjoyed a particular joke, don't worry, this is perfectly normal.
happens to everybody. Simply pass the joke over and return to it later when you are feeling mo
at ease and confident about the joke. It if still fails to amuse you, chat about it with a more intellige
friend or someone who wears glasses. If you fail to enjoy a large proportion of the jokes in this boo
mention it to your local G.P. – he may be able to help.

The joke shown opposite has been broken down into its constituent parts by Dr. Alistair Morri
Professor of Jokes at Loughborough University. Investing ten or twenty minutes in a careful study
this sample joke will pay great dividends in enhancing your enjoyment of the subsequent pages.

FEED LINE

ways read this first – it conveys vital information
cessary to understand the joke. In certain jokes it may
absent, in which case all the necessary information
ll be contained in the illustration itself. (These jokes are
own as Ham Gags). The feed line itself **IS NOT**
INNY, laugh at this and you have completely
sunderstood the joke.

PUNCH LINE

This is the **FUNNY** line and should be read only when
you are confident that you have gained all the requisite
comedy information from the feed line (qv) and/or
illustration. Directly upon reading the punch line the joke
should become apparent and laughter should ensue.
If after ten seconds or so you have failed to laugh, you
have failed to understand the joke and you should start
to read it again from the beginning.

FUNNY MAN

It is the funny man's job to
'carry' the gag, thus 'putting it
across' to the reader. His
delivery of the punch line is the
keystone upon which the
entire joke is hinged, and upon
which it will either stand or fall.
The impact of the punch line is
often accentuated by the
physical appearance of the
funny man. He may wear a
funny hat, have checked
trousers, big ears or some
other visibly amusing
characteristic. In this case the
artist has elected to draw him
badly and with a prominent
nose in order to make it
funnier.

STRAIGHT MAN

ayman's terms it is the job
he straight man to 'tee up'
joke in as humourless a
nner as possible, thus
bling the funny man (qv) to
ver the punch line (qv).
ere the straight man is
ctive, i.e. in a ham gag (qv),
s known as the stooge.

COMEDY PROPS

o known as 'joke furniture', these are specific
ects or items featured in the illustration and
l to the mechanics of the joke. These are the
ls upon which the wheel of comedy spins.

INDICATION LABELS

These are included in order to convey bulk information vital to the
joke, and often to firmly locate the scenario. They many take the
form of folded desk signs, shop signs, fixed wall signs or large
oblong signs suspended from nowhere by two pieces of string.

6

9

10

11

12

13

14

15

18

19

David Addison

22

Famous People On The Toilet

No. 72 Neville Chamberlain

THE GREAT TRAIN ROBBERY
WELL, IT WAS HERE A MINUTE AGO...
ROGER RADIO 87

25

Famous People On The Toilet

No. 97 Magnus Magnusson

27

28

29

30

Famous People On The Toilet

No. 364 Rolf Harris

FISH JOKE

33

CD 19.9.80.

Famous People On The Toilet

No. 129 Jimmy Cricket

36

37

38

39

40

BAD TIT JOKE

43

44

45

47

48

49

JOKE

A man treating his fence with creosote

50

51

52

'REF, CAN YOU CLEAN THE WHITE BALL— I THINK THERE'S A HARE ON IT!'

53

54

LAZY SOD

58

60

61

62

64

SPIDER JOKE

67

Victor Mature

72

73

74

76

77

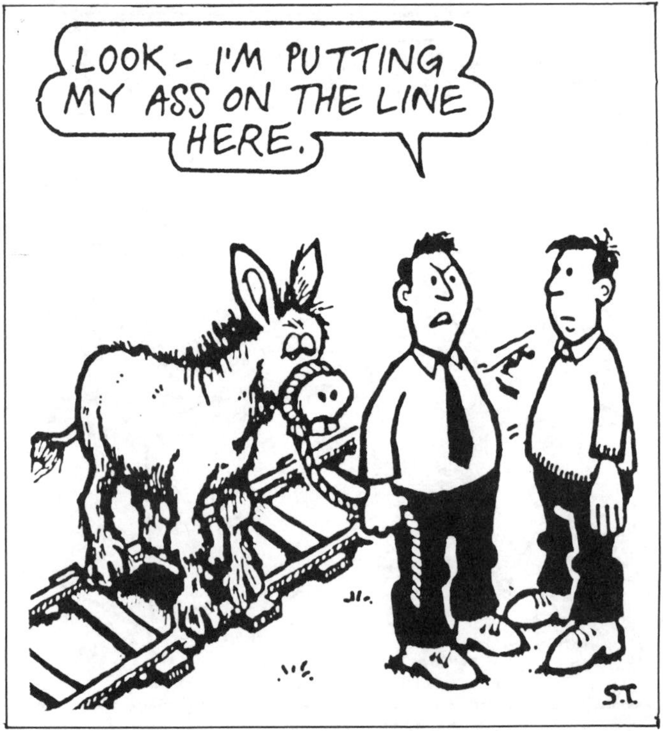
LOOK - I'M PUTTING MY ASS ON THE LINE HERE.
S.T.

Tailors Shop Joke

83

Tailors Shop Joke

85

86

ENEMY PLANE AT 1-0-CLOCK
THAT'S GOOD. WE'VE GOT ½ AN HOUR TO SPARE, THEN
RADIO '81

88

89

91

JOKE INDEX

FURTHER READING

Elementary Joke Comprehension
(Dr A. Morris)
Loughborough Univ. Press, 1972

The Joke Reassessed (Dr A. Morris)
Loughborough Univ. Press, 1974

**Gag Structure & Analysis – A New
Approach** (Dr A. Morris)
Loughborough Univ. Press, 1983

**Women in Jokes: A Post-Feminist
Perspective** (B. Manning)
Sausage Books, (Second Edition) 1986